STABLEMATES

STABLEMATES

THE STORY
OF DICK AND DAISY

Written and Illustrated by

MARGARET S. JOHNSON
and
HELEN LOSSING JOHNSON

hb

New York
HARCOURT, BRACE AND COMPANY

STABLEMATES

CHAPTER I

ONE sunny morning in May a beautiful colt stood by a gate in a green pasture field. His ears were pricked forward and there was an inquiring look in his soft brown eyes, for he was looking for his mother.

All his life Dick had been with her. But now for two weeks he had not seen her; and though there were several other colts in the field with him he still felt lonely. Dick whinnied, hoping for an answer. But none came, and he kicked up his heels and scampered off to join the other colts down by the stream.

The long-legged young horse was nearly a year old. His shining coat was a rich golden chestnut in color; both hind feet were white, and a streak of white ran from his forehead to his velvety nose.

3

The field where Dick and his companions played and grazed and rested in the shade was part of a fine estate in the hills of Virginia. Its pastures and woods covered many acres, and here fine saddle horses were raised and trained for the

4

show and the hunting field. The big brick house stood on a hill looking across a wide valley to a ridge of blue mountains beyond; and the stables and paddocks for the horses were

some distance away from the house. Blithewood, as the estate was called, was famed for its horses, and young Dick would have to learn many things before he took his place among these fine horses. But the lively chestnut colt was still a baby, and as yet he had not learned anything, except to wear a soft leather halter by which he was sometimes led about to accustom him to handling.

The bunch of colts with which Dick had been staying for

two weeks ranged in age from seven or eight months to two years. They were lively youngsters and at first Dick had been rather shy of them and had not joined in their rough play. The older ones were inclined to use their teeth and heels when the play became too wild, and the chestnut colt kept away from them. But he was beginning to find that he could outrun most of the colts, and he enjoyed the wild races from one end to the other of the big pasture.

Once a day hay and a few oats were given to the colts and there was much pushing and shoving for first place along the fence. The younger colts were fed separately and Dick had always taken his place with them. But one day he decided that the hay which the older ones were eating looked better than his, so he pushed in among them. One or two kicked and snapped at him, but Dick boldly kicked back and soon they were all feeding peacefully together. Before long the chestnut colt was one of the leaders of the bunch and he seldom thought of his mother.

But he did not quite forget her, and when one morning in June he heard her familiar call, Dick left his companions and raced to the gate. Looking eagerly towards the stable yard he at last saw his mother; and standing close beside her was a tiny foal, golden in color, with one white hind foot and a white star in her forehead! Dick threw up his head and whinnied and his mother answered softly. Then she touched the little foal with her nose and the two walked to the gate.

With arched neck and quivering nostrils, Dick reached over the gate and laid his nose against his mother's shoulder; then he lowered his head to sniff at his tiny sister. The next instant he jumped back in surprise, for his mother had given him a sharp nip on his neck!

Dick looked at his mother with a puzzled expression in his eyes. She had always been gentle and loving to him. But now the new foal received all her care, and even Dick was not allowed to touch the golden baby.

When his mother led her foal back to the stable, Dick

trotted off and joined the colts in a far corner of the pasture. But each day when the little foal and her mother appeared in the yard the chestnut colt would stand by the gate watching them.

One day Dick was delighted to find that the two had been put in a paddock next to his pasture, where he could see them all the time. As the little foal grew bigger she sometimes left her grazing mother and scampered about the paddock. Once she dared to put her nose through the fence and sniff at her big brother.

The head groom noticed the unusual interest the chestnut colt was taking in the foal, and one day he spoke to Mr. Nelson, the owner of the estate, about it.

"I believe Dick would be happier in the field with those two," said the groom. "The old mare seems friendly enough to him now and he is a gentle youngster. The little foal sure is a *daisy,*" the man added, and thus Dick's sister received her name.

The next morning, while Dick was eating his oats with the other colts, he was surprised to have the groom come up to him and take hold of his halter. He snorted and pulled back but the man snapped a rope on his halter and stroked Dick's nose, talking quietly all the time. Soon he allowed the man to lead him out of the pasture and down a lane to

a gate into a field. Here he was turned loose and after a few playful kicks he stood still, looking interestedly around the new pasture. Several mares with foals by their sides were grazing in the field, and suddenly Dick's ears pricked up; for in the group of mares and foals he saw his mother and little Daisy.

With a joyous neigh Dick galloped over to them. Daisy put out an inquiring nose to her big brother, while their mother looked on quietly. Soon Dick was grazing beside them, and in this green pasture, where oak trees cast a cool shade, began a friendship between the two colts which lasted all their lives.

CHAPTER II

THE summer months went by with hot days and soft warm nights. Sometimes a sharp thunder shower blew across the valley and over the upland pastures, and the mares and their foals would take shelter under a big shed in one corner of the field. Young Dick loved the feel of the warm rain on his chestnut coat, and seldom went in the shed. He paid little attention to any horse but his mother and Daisy, and spent much of his time grazing by himself. But when the horses rested in the shade during the hot noon hours, Dick was always near his sister; and the two often lay down close to each other.

By the end of September Daisy was strong enough to run all over the field, and she would try hard to keep up with Dick's swift gallop. The golden foal looked almost exactly like Dick at her age, except for her lighter color. But that would darken as she grew older, and Mr. Nelson, seeing the two together, remarked,

"Those colts are going to do some winning in the biggest shows some day."

Though real training would not begin for Dick until he was three years old, he was given lessons in leading and standing quietly while the groom stroked and handled him. The first time the man picked up his feet, Dick plunged and snorted; but he was naturally gentle and soon found he was not going to be hurt.

Dick and Daisy were the type of riding horses called "hunters," bred and trained for taking high jumps as they followed the hounds; and from the time they were able to follow their mother about the field the colts were taught to jump over low obstacles.

Dick loved to jump and one morning in October, when the oak and hickory trees were turning scarlet and gold, the chestnut colt proved that he was to be a real hunter. The dew was still on the grass, for the sun had not risen far above the horizon. Dick, who was grazing near the fence in a far corner of the field, heard a sound which was strangely exciting—the clear musical baying of a pack of foxhounds.

Dick threw up his head and looked eagerly in the direction from which the sound came, and in a moment he saw the hounds come over the top of a hill and race down the field towards some woods. The colt was watching the pack with such interest that he did not notice the horses and their riders until they were quite close. When he did finally see them, Dick went wild with excitement. Up and down the fence he galloped, looking for a place to get out. Just then the hounds swerved back towards the pasture, followed by the entire field of riders, and Dick could hear the horses' hard breathing and the squeak of saddle leather. Around the field he raced once more and when he came to the fence he gathered his haunches under him and sailed cleanly over.

Galloping hard, Dick soon caught up with the hunt. But the pace was too swift for such a young horse, and at the next fence he was left behind. When the last rider had disappeared and the voices of the hounds had died away in the distance, Dick trotted slowly back to his own pasture. But without the spur of excitement, the colt made no effort to jump into the field, and it was not until a groom found him and led him through the gate that Dick rejoined his mother and Daisy.

Late that afternoon Mr. Nelson and the head groom came into the pasture. In the groom's hand was a measure of oats, and Dick was the first horse to put his nose deep into the delicious food. While he ate, Mr. Nelson ran his hand down the colt's slim legs and stroked his back and shoulders. Finally he stood back and looked at Dick with a pleased smile.

"There's not a mark on him," he said. "When I saw that colt take the fence as I rode with the hunt this morning, I

was afraid he might have a scraped or swollen ankle to show for it. But he never touched the fence at all. You and I are going to do great things together some day, Dick," he added, and gave the colt a friendly slap on his flank which sent him trotting off to the other horses.

Several times during that autumn Dick heard the distant baying of hounds. But the hunt never came in sight again, and he did not repeat his jump.

In late November rain and cold weather set in and all the horses were kept in the stable at night. Dick was put in a roomy box stall next to his mother and Daisy, and he loved the good hay and oats and bran mash which were fed him.

On sunny days they were turned out in a paddock near the stable and one morning Dick was surprised to find that his mother was not with them. Daisy trotted close to her big brother, looking about worriedly and giving anxious little calls. She was now more than six months old and large enough to be weaned. She and Dick had been put in a paddock with several other colts, and though she missed her mother at first she soon forgot her because she was with Dick.

Thus the two fine colts lived happily and grew handsomer and bigger as the months went by. Out in the big pastures in the summer, or in the warm stable in the winter, they lived a sheltered, carefree life, until the time came for Dick to be trained for the saddle.

CHAPTER III

O N a fresh morning in June, just two years after Dick had first seen his baby sister, the colts were standing in the shade of a big hickory tree near a stream. Dick was now a well-developed three-year-old. His coat was sleek and shining, he held his fine head high on a strong neck, and he had long clean legs and well-muscled hindquarters.

Daisy, being a year younger, was more coltish-looking and a bit more slender in build; but she had the same look of good breeding and intelligence as Dick, and the two colts were a sight to please the eye of any horseman.

The two men now walking across the pasture towards Dick and Daisy were especially pleased with the appearance of the colts, for Mr. Nelson and his head groom were proud of the fine horses raised at Blithewood. Dick lifted his head and whinnied softly when he saw Mr. Nelson, for he had learned to associate his owner's visits with tastes of oats and carrots and other delicacies. Both colts walked up to the men, and when Mr. Nelson snapped a rope on Dick's halter, he followed quietly; but when he was led through the gate and Daisy was left in the pasture, the young horse refused to move and tried to pull away and run back to Daisy.

"Steady now; none of that!" said Mr. Nelson, and he and the groom forced Dick to go with them.

In the small paddock where the men took him the young horse fretted and fussed, and he objected vigorously when they attempted to put a bridle on him. Time and again he shook the hard, unpleasant bit out of his mouth, and he even reared up on his hind legs to get away from it.

But Mr. Nelson and the groom had trained many horses and they persisted gently but firmly until Dick was wearing a bridle for the first time.

Tossing and shaking his head, the spirited young horse

was led around the paddock. But though he tried hard he could not get the bit out of his mouth and he finally grew more quiet.

Dick's lesson did not last long, and each day he was taken up and made to wear a bridle until he became quite accustomed to it. Long reins were next attached to the bridle, and Dick learned to turn and stop at command, and also to jump over low hurdles. By the time his training had progressed as

far as wearing a saddle, Dick began to take pride in doing his work well, and he would arch his neck proudly when Mr. Nelson praised and stroked him.

Thus the weeks went by, and Dick was almost ready for the new experience of carrying a man on his back. Each day, after working in the hot sun, Dick thoroughly enjoyed the rub-down which the groom always gave him. The cool grass in the pasture felt especially delightful and the young horse rolled vigorously each time he was turned out with Daisy.

One warm night when the moon, shining through soft clouds, gave a pale light, Dick and Daisy got out of the pasture. A little-used gate at the far end of the field was not fastened, and Dick, pausing for an instant to scratch his neck against it, pushed it open wide enough to get through. With Daisy following close behind, the young horse walked quietly down a lane, gazing about him with shining eyes. A rabbit scampered in front of him, and Dick shied violently to one side, and both colts galloped for a short distance, snorting and kicking. At last they quieted down and then they saw that on the other side of the fence was a field of oats just beginning to turn golden with the ripened grain. Both young horses tried to snatch a delicious mouthful by stretching their necks over the fence as far as possible, but the oats were just out of reach. Dick began to trot up and down, looking for a place to get in the field, while Daisy watched him. Suddenly the long-legged young hunter, who had been learning to take higher jumps each day in his training, gathered his hind legs under him and leaped clear over the fence into the oatfield.

The partly ripened grain came above Dick's knees, and he snatched it up in greedy mouthfuls. He was so absorbed in eating his fill of oats that he did not notice that Daisy had not attempted to jump into the field.

As it turned out for both colts, it was fortunate that Daisy stayed in the lane. Green oats are a dangerous diet for horses, and Dick was stuffing himself with them as fast as he could.

The young horse had trampled and pulled up a good many oats before he began to feel uncomfortable. He took a few more lazy nibbles, and then walked slowly over to the fence where he rubbed noses with Daisy. She whinnied softly and started to walk away, but Dick did not feel like jumping over into the lane. Instead, he soon lay down and began to groan as he rolled over on his side. The pain grew worse, and if help did not come soon, fine young Dick would be a very sick horse.

But there was no man near, and all Daisy could do was to gallop up and down the lane neighing wildly. In the end, however, it was Daisy's frantic neighs that saved Dick.

Mr. Nelson had been out late and he was getting into bed when he heard Daisy's distant calls. There was something so worried in the sound that Mr. Nelson was alarmed. Hastily putting on his clothes he went out and woke one of the men and soon they were running across the fields towards Dick and Daisy. With great difficulty the men managed to get Dick on his feet and they pulled down a part of the fence to lead him into the lane. Daisy followed anxiously as Mr. Nelson and the groom forced Dick to walk back to the stable. Many times the young horse tried to lie down; but at last he was in a box stall and the quickly summoned veterinary was examining him. All night the three men worked over him. By morning Dick was out of danger, and in a day or two he was quite well again. But if Daisy had not given the warning, Dick might have died on that warm moonlight night.

When, after a week's rest, Dick was again saddled and bridled and put over the jumps, he was especially lively, and trotted gaily with his head and tail held high.

"Let's see how he likes a weight on his back," Mr. Nelson said to the groom; and while the man held Dick's head, Mr. Nelson suddenly put his foot in the stirrup, and before Dick realized what was happening he was in the saddle. For an instant the young horse stood still. Then he gave a leap forward and stood on his hind legs. But his rider's firm, light hold on the reins, and the strong pressure of his knees on Dick's sides, soon gave the horse confidence, and within an hour the young hunter was proudly carrying his owner about the paddock.

In the days that followed Dick learned to go all about the big estate with Mr. Nelson on his back, and when he found he could take a rider over low jumps, the chestnut hunter grew to love this work more than anything else.

So far, all Dick's work had been in the grassy pastures and soft earth of the lanes of Blithewood, and he had not needed any shoes; but there would be danger of cracking his fine hoofs if he trotted on stony roads or jumped a fence on rough and rocky ground.

Thus it was that one morning when he was taken into the stable yard Dick saw a strange man getting out of a car. The young horse shied away from the anvil and small forge which the blacksmith set down near him. He snorted and jumped when the stranger picked up one of his front feet

and began trying the size of different light iron shoes on his hoof. The groom tried to hold Dick quiet so that the black-smith could trim his hoofs; but it was not until Mr. Nelson came out and petted and soothed the trembling young hunter that Dick was finally shod on all four feet.

At first even the light shoes felt heavy, but he soon grew accustomed to them, and by the time cool weather came again in early October, Dick was ready for his first experience with the hunt.

CHAPTER IV

EARLY one clear autumn morning Dick was taken out of the stable, saddled and bridled, and with two older hunters he was led up to the door of the big house. Mr. Nelson soon came out with two friends and the three mounted and trotted down the driveway.

The crisp air, the company of the other horses, and a feeling of excitement in the little group made young Dick very skittish. He tossed his head and pranced along sideways, switching his tail and pulling on the reins.

"You had better save some of that energy for the hunt, young fellow," said Mr. Nelson. "I'm taking you for your first experience today because the hounds meet near by."

"Steady, now!" he added, as Dick broke into a lively canter.

Suddenly the young horse threw up his head and his ears pricked forward excitedly. A short distance ahead was an open field, and in that field Dick saw many horses and riders standing or moving slowly about. But the sight that most thrilled Dick was the pack of hounds. These hounds were bunched so closely together that their black and tan and white backs looked like a moving carpet, above which their tails waved gaily. Every once in a while a hound wandered away from the pack only to be sternly ordered back by one of the "whippers-in."

This hunt to which Mr. Nelson belonged was called a "drag hunt," which means that a trail for the hounds was made by dragging a bag of aniseed, the scent of which the hounds love to follow, over many miles of country. The woods and mountains were rough and a fox would lead the pack into places where horses and riders could not go, so an aniseed trail was made across country in places where it was possible for horses to follow. There were many stiff jumps

on the way and anyone who followed these hounds for a day would be considered an excellent rider.

Mr. Nelson kept Dick some distance away from the other riders, for the young hunter was much excited by the sight and scent of so many horses and hounds.

When the pack was finally sent on, Dick tried hard to follow, and it took strong hands and good riding to hold him back.

As the first hound picked up the trail of the aniseed bag and gave tongue, Dick leaped forward and, for the length of two fields, the young hunter led the rest of the horses. A low fence was taken easily and then Dick saw ahead of him a most difficult jump. Several of the other hunters were galloping close behind him now and for a moment the young horse lost his head. In spite of Mr. Nelson's steadying hand and voice, Dick did not slow up as he came to the high rail fence, and though his front feet cleared it, his hind feet hit the top rail, almost throwing him on his nose as he landed

on a rough patch of ground. Mr. Nelson quieted the excited horse, while the rest of the hunters galloped by. Then he urged Dick after them and made him take one more easy jump, for he did not want the young hunter to be made nervous the first time he went out with the hunt.

Dick was wet with sweat and still excited when he reached the stable yard an hour later, but after a rub-down he walked quietly into his stall beside Daisy and touched noses with his sister when she whinnied softly to him.

During the autumn Mr. Nelson gave Dick many a run with the hounds, and the chestnut hunter learned to control his excitement and obey his rider's guidance in taking hard jumps. He also learned to ride in a horse trailer drawn behind a car when the hunt met a long distance from Blithewood. This was a terrifying experience for the young horse and he balked completely the first time Mr. Nelson and the groom tried to persuade him to walk up the slight incline into the trailer. At last someone thought of bringing Daisy out, and her presence seemed to reassure Dick, for he at last gingerly entered what seemed to him a very queer stall. To everyone's surprise, slim golden Daisy insisted upon following her brother and, as it was a two-horse trailer, she was allowed to stay. For a few times after that Dick and Daisy rode together, but before long Dick lost all fear and went alone.

Though Dick loved the hunt he always returned home more eagerly than he set out, for his greatest joy lay in his companionship with Daisy.

Late one chilly, rainy afternoon Dick came in from a canter across the muddy countryside. He was tired and hungry and he ate several mouthfuls of hay before glancing over into Daisy's stall for the usual friendly greetings. But Daisy was not there, and Dick threw up his head and looked quickly about the big stable. The warm sweet-smelling stable was growing dark in the early twilight and the horses which were contentedly munching hay in the row of stalls were only dim shapes. Horses can see well in the dark, however, and Dick soon found that Daisy was not in the stable. Giving a worried neigh, he began to paw the floor of his stall with an impatient front foot. Soon a man came in to give the horses their evening feed of oats and found Dick too restless to eat. All night the young hunter fussed and called, and the next morning when Mr. Nelson took him out for exercise,

Dick was nervous and jumpy.

In the evening Daisy returned from the horse show, where she had been entered in a class of hunter colts, and Dick greeted her with delight. Daisy, too, seemed happy to be home, and Mr. Nelson shook his head as he watched them.

"I have never seen such devotion between two horses before," he said. "I wonder what would happen if they ever had to be separated. But then we will hope that that time will never come," he added, as he thoughtfully stroked the shining white streak on Dick's nose.

The grass and trees were again fresh and green in the spring when Dick, now a well-trained four-year-old, was first exhibited in a horse show. For two weeks he had been having special training and care, and he had become expert in taking the different types of jumps which a finished show hunter is expected to perform.

The chestnut hunter was given cross country runs, too, to

harden his muscles, and one day he was delighted to have Daisy as his companion on one of these exercise gallops. The beautiful young mare was being trained this spring, just as Dick had been the year before, and was now for the first time carrying a rider. With Dick as a guide, Daisy learned quickly and soon sailed over the fences almost as easily as her brother; but she was a bit more nervous and high-strung than Dick and needed careful riding.

When Dick was taken from his trailer at the big outdoor show one warm morning, he gazed about with an interested expression in his brown eyes. As he stood with his head held high and ears pricked forward, Dick made a perfect picture of a fine hunter.

"If that horse can perform as well as he looks, you have a winner there," one of the exhibitors remarked to Mr. Nelson.

"I know he will do his best," Dick's owner answered, stroking the horse's shining neck affectionately, and Dick's velvety nostrils quivered as he rubbed his nose against Mr. Nelson's coat.

When Dick went into the ring, he tried in every way to do his best. He studied each jump carefully as he approached it, and went over without a fault the first time around; but the burst of applause which greeted his performance startled the young hunter, and the next time he rushed at the highest jump too fast and hit the top rail with one hind foot. The third time was again perfect, though he hesitated at the last jump for an instant before clearing it nicely. Horse after horse was put around the course and each made more faults than Dick.

Mr. Nelson was beginning to hope that he had won a first prize when a fine gray hunter, veteran of many a show ring and hunting field, made a perfect score, and Dick was given a second prize. However, this was a real triumph for a young horse at his first show, and Dick found an especially delicious feed of oats and bran waiting in his manger when he reached his comfortable home stall that night.

Many times during the next two years Dick and Daisy won prizes in shows, and Dick became well known as Mr. Nelson's favorite mount in the hunting field. The chestnut hunter had developed into a wise and sensible horse and he was sometimes given as a safe mount to ladies who were visitors at Blithewood. But Dick always preferred to have his owner on his back and when Daisy was galloping by his side, he was completely happy.

The life on the big farm was an ideal one for a horse— plenty of good food and careful grooming, wide pastures and warm stables; the excitement of the hunt and the companionship of Daisy and the other horses. Dick might have lived uneventfully to a peaceful old age at Blithewood but for an accident which happened one damp afternoon in late November, when he was well over six years old.

CHAPTER V

THE hunt met a long distance from Blithewood on that gray November day, and Dick and Daisy looked about interestedly when they stepped out of the trailer, for this part of the country was new to them.

Dick was, as usual, eager to be off; but he had learned to wait quietly until the signal was given for the riders to follow the hounds, and only his quickly moving ears and switching tail showed his impatience. The chestnut hunter was disappointed when a young lady mounted him instead of Mr. Nelson. Daisy had been loaned to a friend of Mr. Nelson's for the day, and the young mare fretted and fussed when she felt a stranger's hand on the reins.

At last the pack was off and the group of riders followed. Down a gentle slope Dick and Daisy cantered and jumped lightly over a brook at the foot of the hill. A straight-away gallop across a level pasture came next, and then there was a gate to be cleared. Daisy was now ahead of Dick, going too fast and rushing at the jumps. The young man on her back was inclined to be a reckless rider and did not curb the spirited young mare as he should. When the hounds disappeared into a small wood, the riders pulled up and waited for the pack to untangle the trail. Dick stood quietly listening for the clear baying which would show that the trail had been straightened out, and he was the first horse to start off after the hounds. The young lady riding Dick was delighted with her mount and let him do much as he pleased, for she found that he knew all the rules of hunting.

After an hour's run, Dick, cantering easily across the hill-top field, suddenly realized that something was wrong. The baying of the hounds grew louder and more excited, and they increased their speed as they turned down the hill. The leading hound was yelping now, and soon everyone saw a

fox streaking towards a tangle of blackberry bushes on the edge of a wood.

Most of the riders tried to stop their horses, for they realized the hounds had left the trail of the aniseed bag to chase after the fox, while the huntsmen tried vainly to stop the runaway pack.

Then Dick saw Daisy going at a furious gallop close behind the hounds, and he dashed off in pursuit. Through the bushes and over a fence poured the hounds, and Daisy's rider turned her sharply to find a suitable place for a jump. Just as the young mare gathered herself together to leap, a startled pheasant flew up, almost striking her head. Daisy hesitated, then crashed into the fence and fell heavily, throwing her rider. Too close behind to stop himself, Dick, with a magnificent leap, cleared the fallen horse, then stopped and stood trembling and snorting, while his frightened rider clung to the reins.

Daisy's rider was soon on his feet, shaken but unhurt, and with others helping him, he tried to get Daisy to stand up. But though she struggled, she did not seem able to rise.

When Mr. Nelson arrived he found one man holding Dick, while several others worked with Daisy.

Dick whinnied when he saw Mr. Nelson and took a step towards him; Daisy, too, seemed to recognize her owner's voice and lay still, breathing hard.

Mr. Nelson examined Daisy carefully. "I doubt if there are any broken bones," he said; "but there is something the matter. Come, Daisy, get up, girl," he added, pulling on her bridle. With a snort, the young mare finally struggled to her feet, and then it was seen that her right front leg was scraped and bleeding from knee to ankle, and was beginning to swell. When she tried to walk, she limped painfully, hardly touching her right foot to the ground. Dick whinnied softly and touched Daisy's neck with his nose. He was still trembling, and he shied violently when Mr. Nelson quickly mounted him. As his owner urged him gently forward, Dick began walking slowly, and then he found that Mr. Nelson was leading poor Daisy close by his side. Stopping often to rest Daisy's injured leg, and proceeding very slowly, Dick, with Mr. Nelson on his back and Daisy leaning against him, finally reached the road where the trailer was waiting for them.

Rain began to fall before they reached Blithewood and the task of getting Daisy out of the trailer was made more difficult by the downpour. Finally, the injured mare was safely in her stall next to Dick's, and the chestnut hunter, with a sigh of contentment, began eating hay. Now that he and Daisy were in the comfortable stalls, Dick felt safe, as horses always do in the home stable. But his contentment vanished when the veterinary joined Mr. Nelson and the groom in the next stall, and he snorted nervously at the strong smell of antiseptics.

At last the men left and Dick dozed fitfully in the quiet stable, occasionally giving a soft little call when Daisy stirred.

The next morning Daisy was still lying down in her stall. Her right front leg had been badly strained and it would be some time before it could be seen whether she would fully recover.

"I'm thankful you were not hurt, Dick," said Mr. Nelson. "Come along now and I will put you over a few jumps to cure any nervousness from yesterday's accident."

Dick started off at his usual swinging trot and broke into a lazy canter when Mr. Nelson turned him through a gate into a large field. Straight towards the fence on the other side went Dick, and he felt Mr. Nelson's knees tighten against his sides in preparation for the jump. But just as he was ready to leap, he remembered yesterday's crash as Daisy went down, and felt again the fear which came over him when it seemed that he would jump directly on her. Suddenly bracing all four legs, Dick stopped with his chest touching the fence, and Mr. Nelson almost went on over his head.

Twice more Mr. Nelson tried to put Dick over the fence, but each time he refused and stood sweating and trembling, fearing imaginary dangers.

Finally, his owner rode Dick back to the stable and stood by while the groom unsaddled him.

"Perhaps a few days' rest will make you forget your fear," Mr. Nelson said gravely, and gave orders that Dick was to be turned out in a pasture for several days.

The chestnut hunter was lonely in the pasture and he was happy when Mr. Nelson again mounted him and went out through the gates of Blithewood. This time Dick was not asked to jump, and during an hour's ride he was his usual spirited, well-mannered self.

Two days later Mr. Nelson again put Dick at a jump, this time an easy one, with the same result—absolute refusal and a nervous trembling. The fine horse felt much upset because he could not do as Mr. Nelson wished. His willing spirit had taken him gaily on long hard runs and over the most difficult obstacles, and he had had a real pride in obeying his rider.

As a riding horse Dick was still perfect, and so Mr. Nelson decided not to try to make him jump until Daisy was able to go with him.

But as the weeks went by and Daisy's leg remained stiff and slightly bent, Mr. Nelson sadly realized that the valuable young mare would never jump again. She might be used as a saddle horse, but her hunting and prize-winning days were over before they had fairly begun.

CHAPTER VI

THE cold storms of winter were giving way to warm sunshine in late February before Mr. Nelson finally gave up trying to make Dick jump again and realized that his value as a hunter was over.

Dick himself was happy with Daisy in the stall beside him, or out in the paddock on sunny days, and he enjoyed the daily gallops with Mr. Nelson or the groom on his back. But several times during the winter when he heard the hounds on a distant trail, he became nervous and excited and quieted down only when he reached the stable.

Mr. Nelson was fond of Dick but he was deeply disappointed at the failure of the fine hunter to overcome his fear, and he at last decided to sell Dick, if he could be sure of a good home for him.

One afternoon Dick, half dozing in his stall, heard Mr. Nelson's voice and, looking up, saw that there was a stranger with his master. The two men stopped at Dick's stall and Mr. Nelson stroked the velvety nose which the hunter stretched out in greeting. "Here he is; we will take him out so that you can try him," said Mr. Nelson, and led Dick from the stable.

Soon the stranger, mounted on Dick, and Mr. Nelson, on another horse, were cantering down the driveway and out on the road. Before they returned, they had gone for several miles on a rough woodland road and had climbed a steep path on a rocky hillside. Dick was rather surprised at his rider's choice of country, for he was not accustomed to quite such rough ground. But he went willingly and obediently and picked his way very carefully over stones and around fallen trees, and the young man looked pleased when he dismounted in the stable yard.

"He is just what I want," he exclaimed; "handsome, gentle, and well-trained; and sure-footed, too! I will take him with me when I go West next week."

Mr. Nelson's friend, Jack Davis, owned a big cattle ranch in the mountains of Colorado. Its many acres of wild pasture and woods, streams and a lake, made an ideal spot for people who enjoyed an outdoor vacation. So young Davis had decided to start a dude ranch, a place where people could have horseback riding, hiking, fishing, and swimming in the cool, clear mountain air. He already owned a bunch of cow ponies, many of which were gentle enough for inexperienced riders. But he wanted one or two "fancy" eastern horses, as he called them, for people who were particular about their mounts. As there would be no jumping, Dick fitted in perfectly, and Mr. Nelson knew that his friend would give the fine hunter a good home.

When, several days later, Dick was led into a trailer, he went quietly, glancing back once to see if Daisy were following; but she was still in the stable, so when Dick looked for the last time at the place where he had lived so many happy years, his sister was not with him.

Dick did not feel worried until he was taken off the trailer in the freight yard of the nearest city. Engines were puffing and backing, shunting cars from one part of the yard to another, and Dick threw up his head and snorted in alarm.

"Steady there, old fellow," said young Davis, patting Dick's neck reassuringly. "No one is going to hurt you," he added, as the chestnut hunter started violently. Another man had quietly walked up to Dick and now took hold of the bridle. He was dressed as a cowboy and had come East with Jack to help take back the horses.

"The other horse is in the car, boss," said the cowboy, as he started to lead Dick towards a freight car. "Come on now!" he added, when the hunter pulled back.

Dick, as always, wanted to do what was asked of him; but this time it really seemed impossible for him to obey. Mr. Nelson, or the Blithewood groom, had always handled him, and he was beginning to wonder where Daisy was. Now these two strangers wanted him to walk up a steep incline into a dark freight car, and Dick balked. But he was not allowed to refuse to obey for very long—Jack Davis again took his head and coaxed and encouraged him, until his front feet were on the incline. Suddenly, the cowboy cracked a whip at Dick's heels and the hunter plunged up and into the car. Once in, he stood trembling and then relaxed, as he saw and smelled another horse. He gave a low whinny as he walked into the improvised stall; but the other saddle horse only glanced at Dick and kept on munching his hay.

When the train started with a jerk, Dick snorted and trembled again; but the two men steadied him, so he grew more quiet and, by the time it was dark, hunger drove him to eat part of his portion of oats.

During the three days' trip Dick became more accustomed to the steady progress of the train. The cowboy slept in the car with the horses and took good care of them, and

as the train speeded on into the western mountains and it grew colder, he put heavy blankets on the horses.

Dick was weary of the constant traveling and homesick for Daisy and Blithewood by the time Jack Davis led him off the train at a small station; but he held his head high and looked about with alert interest. Soon the two horses were in a trailer, and after an hour's drive they reached their new home.

Below them, on a wide plateau, lay the Yellow Pine Ranch. Beyond the fields and forested slopes rose snow-

covered peaks, and around a long log house clustered several cabins. The sheds and barns were surrounded by roughly fenced corrals, and in one of these corrals were a few horses. The cold, clear March sunshine gleamed on patches of snow in the higher fields, and there were pools of water left by melting snow on the low ground near the stream. There was a feeling of exhilaration in the mountain air, and Dick, happy to be free from trailers and freight cars, tossed his head and kicked up a bit as Jack led him away to the stable.

Dick's new stall was not like his big roomy one at Blithewood, but it was warm in the stable, his manger was filled with hay, and soon he was given some oats. This new home was comfortable, but as he half dozed in the quiet warmth, Dick felt lonely, for he missed the happy companionship with Daisy.

CHAPTER VII

MARCH went by, with bright, chill days, occasional rains, and once a real snow storm, and by the early part of April Dick was more at home in his new surroundings. For a few days after his arrival, he rested in the stable; then he was turned out with the cow ponies in the corral.

At Blithewood the horses had been high-spirited animals, but they were well-bred and gentle-mannered and seldom bit or kicked when in the pasture together.

Dick was eager for companionship and he trotted confidently towards the horses which were eating hay in a corner of the big corral. With a friendly whinny the hunter joined a spotted horse, and put down his head to nibble at the hay. Suddenly, the spotted horse whirled and planted a well-aimed kick on Dick's ribs; and only the fact that the cow

pony had no shoes on his hind feet saved Dick from a painful injury. As it was, the kick hurt severely and Dick jumped away with an astonished snort. All his friendly feelings vanished, and though afterwards he spent most of his time in the corral with the other horses, he did not go near them.

Sometimes Dick would stand by the gate and call again and again; then listen, with pricked ears and eager eyes. But an answering whinny from Daisy never came, and after a while he gave up looking for her.

During the bright spring days Dick learned to look forward to trips about the surrounding country with Jack Davis on his back. At first he disliked the heavy western saddle, and the bridle with the curb bit bothered him. But after he became accustomed to them, he willingly learned to follow rough mountain trails and a hard gallop across an upland pasture delighted the chestnut hunter.

One thing which Dick would never submit to was being roped like the other horses. He had always been accustomed to go up to anyone who came out in the pasture at Blithewood and allow himself to be led away; but cow ponies must be roped to be caught, and when Dick saw the whirling rope in the hands of a cowboy, he galloped away in fear and could not be caught until he, too, was roped. For the first time in his life Dick fought wildly, kicking and struggling, and when at last he was subdued, Jack Davis forbade anyone to go near him again with a rope.

It took much coaxing and petting and offerings of oats to make the chestnut hunter forget this indignity.

One morning Jack saddled Dick and, with several cowboys, started off to drive the big herd of white-faced cattle up to the high summer pastures. As usual, the cow ponies bucked cheerfully for a few minutes when they were first mounted, and Dick looked on in surprise. The well-trained hunter could never understand why these horses acted in such an unmannerly fashion, and he laid his ears back and snapped at any horse that came near him. But these same ponies knew their job and turned and twisted as they galloped swiftly to head off a wild cow. When a cow was roped, they braced themselves for the jerk and stood still, pulling hard, until released.

Dick scorned the cattle and paid no attention to them. He had sometimes seen a few cows in the fields of Virginia, but they always galloped away from the horses and hounds. Today, however, he was to learn that some cows are not so harmless.

The sun grew warm as the day advanced and by the time the upland pasture was reached, Dick was hot and thirsty. A tiny icy cold stream from a far snow peak ran through the pasture, and Dick was drinking from it when a shout from one of the cowboys startled Jack Davis. The next instant he jerked up Dick's head and struck him with his whip; for a maddened cow which had somehow lost sight of her calf was charging straight at Dick.

Terrified at the first lash from a whip which he had ever

received, Dick leaped forward and tore away at a swift gallop; but the cow was swift, too, and was almost upon them when young Davis turned Dick so quickly that he slipped and nearly fell. The cow swung her head in passing and grazed the hunter's flank with her horn, leaving a red streak in the shining coat. Before she could catch up with Dick and his rider again, one of the cowboys roped the cow and then chased her back to the herd.

The chestnut hunter was nervous and winded when Jack brought him to a standstill, and he kept pricking his ears towards the herd, with a startled expression in his eyes. The scratch on Dick's flank healed in a few days but he never forgot the wild cow.

In June guests began to arrive at the Yellow Pine Ranch and Dick's life became one of busy routine. In the chill of early mornings the riding horses were brought up from the night pasture, fed some grain, and saddled for the day's work. Handsome big Dick was in great demand, but young

Davis gave him only to good riders, for he did not want the fine hunter spoiled. Many of the other horses were very gentle, even rather lazy, and so were good for inexperienced and young riders.

Soon after breakfast a gay party would gather at the main ranch house waiting for their mounts to be brought to them. Often the trips were long and the trails rough, but Dick always tried to get ahead of the other horses and his longer legs enabled him to walk faster up steep hills.

Once, for two weeks, Dick had a very heavy man for a rider. This man insisted upon going on the longest rides and the chestnut hunter was tired and thinner by the time he left.

Though Dick performed his work cheerfully and well, all the keen enjoyment which he had felt in a canter across the fields with Daisy, or a long hard run after the hounds, had left him. He was well fed but not as carefully as at Blithewood, and there was not much time for grooming. He was in good condition, and if he could have had a real com-

panion, he would have been quite happy.

But no horse could take Daisy's place, and as the months went by Dick became less spirited and his brown eyes lost their alert expression.

Then one glorious morning in August, Dick met a new rider, and a different life began for the chestnut hunter.

CHAPTER VIII

THE slender girl who was waiting to mount Dick one morning had come with her father to stay for a month at the Yellow Pine Ranch. She was an expert horsewoman, and in the stable of her home in New York State were several saddle horses.

As Dick put down his head to sniff at Eleanor Strong's outstretched hands, Jack Davis smiled.

"I thought you would like each other," he said. "You know the real thing in a saddle horse, Miss Strong, and you will soon find that Dick has been well trained."

Then he told Eleanor about the accident which had spoiled Dick as a jumper.

The chestnut hunter started off gaily with Eleanor's light weight on his back, and her gentle yet firm handling of the reins reminded Dick of the riders he had carried in Virginia. By the end of their first day together the two were firm friends, and Dick greeted Eleanor with a soft whinny when she came out to the corral the next morning. In the girl's pocket Dick found a lump of sugar, and he crunched it with delight.

Soon Eleanor had begged a currycomb and brush from one of the cowboys and was grooming Dick's chestnut coat. Dick thoroughly enjoyed the petting and care which Eleanor Strong gave him and he learned to look eagerly for her each morning. On Sundays, when all the saddle horses were given a day of rest, the girl would go down to the corral and sit on the fence, and while Dick sniffed at her pockets for sugar she would stroke his shining neck and the white streak on his nose and talk quietly to him.

"I think if I owned you I could persuade you to jump again, Dickie," she said thoughtfully one day as Dick rubbed his velvet nose against her cheek.

The Strongs had been at the ranch nearly four weeks when a party started off one morning for a two-day pack-trip into the mountains. Several quiet, steady horses carried the packs of camp equipment and provisions, while each of the eight guests who made up the party rode their favorite. horse. With the guide and "horse wranglers" the group made quite a procession as they wound across the meadows towards an upland trail.

Eleanor Strong rode Dick and the chestnut hunter shook his head and switched his tail as he cantered off in the chill morning air. The fresh breeze smelled of pines and spruces and distant snow peaks glistened in the sun. When the trail grew steeper Dick slowed down to a walk and followed the sure-footed cow pony, which was in the lead. A large herd of cattle grazing in a hillside pasture moved away when they saw the horses and riders; once in a wooded spot a deer leaped through the trees, and on a distant rocky slope could be seen moving specks which the guide said were wild

mountain sheep.

After a stop for lunch the party went on and by four o'clock had reached the place where camp was to be made for the night.

Dick was glad to be unsaddled and turned out in a green mountain meadow with the other horses. As it grew dark, however, he wandered back towards the camp fire under the spruce and pine trees and was rewarded by the usual lump of sugar from Eleanor.

A ride up to the timberline, where the trees grew smaller and finally disappeared altogether when the altitude became too high for them, occupied the next morning. The guide urged Eleanor to ride one of the cow ponies, for there was no trail and Dick had not had any experience in mountain climbing. But the girl insisted upon riding the hunter and he carried her carefully and safely, though he snorted disapprovingly at some of the places he was asked to climb.

After lunch while the cowboys were packing camp equipment in preparation for the homeward trip, Eleanor slipped away from the others and went over to Dick as he stood tied to a tree saddled and ready to go.

"Dickie, darling," said the girl, leaning her cheek against

the hunter's shining neck, "this is our last long ride to-gether; let's go off by ourselves for a while."

No one saw Eleanor go and as her father had stayed at the ranch, she was not missed until an hour or more later when the group was ready to leave for home.

Meanwhile Dick was cantering gaily across a sloping meadow and soon Eleanor turned him into a pine wood where the sweet-smelling needles made a soft carpet.

The light was dim under the trees and Dick shied and snorted when a squirrel burst into angry chattering above his head. He walked faster when he saw the sun shining through the trees ahead, and soon they came out into an opening filled with rocks and bushes.

Dick was picking his way across this clearing when sud-denly a furry black bear cub burst out from almost under his feet and rushed away. Before the frightened hunter could gather himself together a big black bear with another cub at her heels trotted out of the woods. The bear gave an angry "woof" when she saw Dick and Eleanor, and the horse, completely terrified, reared and plunged and, in spite of the girl's efforts to control him, galloped wildly across the clearing and into the woods.

Bending down to avoid the low branches, Eleanor managed to stay in the saddle for a short distance. Then a branch caught in her coat and she was swept off almost under the hunter's flying hoofs. The sudden loss of his rider added to Dick's panic and he made several more wild leaps before stopping. Then he turned and, wild-eyed and snorting, walked slowly back to Eleanor.

The girl lay perfectly still and Dick put down his head and sniffed gently at her face. When there was no response, he pushed his nose against her shoulder trying to wake the unconscious girl. Worried and unhappy, Dick stood close to Eleanor, his nervously moving ears and dilated nostrils showing that he still feared the bears.

But in spite of his fear, Dick did not leave his fallen rider,

and when Eleanor finally opened her eyes she saw Dick's nose close to her face and felt his soft breath on her cheek. She sat up and then realized what had happened. By clinging to Dick's bridle and then to his neck she was able to stand up, and at last managed to lead the hunter to a fallen log. From the log Eleanor tried to climb on Dick's back, but she was so weak and shaken that at first she could not make it.

The gentle, intelligent horse helped in every way he could; stepping lightly, he edged close to the log and stood absolutely still until Eleanor, after several efforts, finally settled herself in the saddle and told him to go on. Through the woods and out into the upland pasture Dick carried his half-conscious rider, walking so slowly and carefully that she was not shaken at all. The girl had lost all sense of direction and trusted to Dick to take her back to camp. The hunter was steadily making his way in the right direction when he suddenly whinnied loudly and was answered by a shout from the cowboy guide.

Two of the men who had been searching in all directions for Eleanor now took her back to camp. Stimulants and a short rest soon revived her and she was able to make her way home to the ranch with the others.

Dick spent the rest of that night in the warm stable and his feed of grain was extra large. But though he was comfortable and well fed, the hunter was lonely, and more than once during the night he gave the soft call that Daisy had always answered in the happy days at Blithewood.

After Eleanor Strong had gone to bed that night, her father sat beside her, talking of the accident and rejoicing that the girl had not been badly injured.

"Dickie was wonderful, Father," said the girl. "He is the nicest horse I ever knew. *Please* let me have him for my own, and take him home with me!"

Mr. Strong did not need another saddle horse but he felt that Dick had shown much intelligence and courage that day and his daughter had grown to love the handsome chestnut hunter. So he at last consented, and thus it was that in a few days Dick was again in a freight car, this time speeding eastward.

CHAPTER IX

DURING the months when Dick was learning to adjust himself to the life on a mountain ranch, Daisy, too, was having new experiences.

When the weather became warm enough, Mr. Nelson ordered Daisy's shoes to be taken off and she was put into a pasture where the turf was soft and the grass was thick and tender. Here on the soft ground all stiffness at last left her injured leg. Before many weeks had passed, a scar and a slight bend at the knee were the only signs left of the terrible fall she had taken when she last hunted with her brother.

At first Daisy missed Dick and her high strong call for her lost companion rang out many times in the days after he left.

One warm May afternoon Daisy was standing under a tree in the pasture, enjoying the cool shade, when she saw Mr. Nelson and a man walking towards her. Hoping for a taste of carrots or oats she galloped up to the men, and Mr. Nelson's friend remarked on her good looks.

"I wish I had a saddle horse like that for my boy," he said, and Mr. Nelson looked thoughtful.

"Well," he said at last, "I am willing to sell her. She is a spirited mare but gentle, and she has always been kindly treated. I think she would be just right for your son."

Daisy's new owner lived in New York City, but they took her to the country for the summer. In the autumn, when they all went back to town, Daisy was put in a livery stable, and her young owner rode her in Central Park.

The spirited mare fretted at the confinement of the stable. There were no more gallops over the meadows at Blithewood, or long days spent grazing and resting under the trees. Three or four times a week Daisy was taken for a canter on the bridle paths of the park; but this was not enough exercise for her, and she became rather lively for a boy to manage.

One day when Daisy was trotting briskly along a bridle path, shaking her head in an effort to make her young rider loosen the reins, a dog suddenly darted across in front of her and dashed over the grass in pursuit of a squirrel. The sight of the fleeing dog was too much for Daisy's self-control, and she whirled and galloped after him, delighted to feel the soft turf under her hoofs again.

The mare's cross-country run did not last very long for a mounted policeman stopped her and brought her back to the bridle path. Though the boy was not thrown, it was decided that unless she had more exercise Daisy was too lively for him to ride. At last his father arranged with the livery stable owner to have the mare hired out to different riders during the week. This would give her the needed exercise and she would be easier for the boy to handle during the week-ends, which was the only time he could ride.

Daisy did not enjoy the arrangement at all. Some of her riders jerked and pulled at her sensitive mouth, others rode poorly, jogging heavily up and down in the saddle. Though she was well fed and cared for, Daisy was not happy, and performed her work in a spiritless manner. As the months went by she became known as a most reliable mount, and was given to less experienced riders. Anyone who had seen Daisy on the day more than a year ago when she led the field of riders in a wild dash after the hounds and made her fatal leap, would not have recognized the quiet horse which trotted along the tame bridle paths of the park.

CHAPTER X

DICK arrived at his new home on a rainy September afternoon. A groom took him off the freight car, and rode him the six miles out of town to the Strongs' farm, which was on a hill about a mile back from the main road. The chestnut hunter trotted slowly along, sniffing delightedly as the damp air brought scents of fields and woods which reminded him of Blithewood.

When the groom turned him into a long driveway, and the big house and barns came into view, Dick quickened his steps. A stable meant food and shelter, and perhaps Daisy would be there too! Then a horse whinnied, and Dick answered happily. Through the open stable door, he could see a horse's head looking inquiringly over the side of a stall. Though he was disappointed that the horse was not Daisy,

Dick was pleased to see a friendly horse again. When the groom led him into a comfortable box stall, Dick began contentedly eating hay, glad to be once more in a big stable which was filled with scents of grain and hay and well-groomed horses.

Under the care of the old groom, Dick soon began to regain his looks. His chestnut coat gleamed like satin, and his mane and forelock, which had grown long and tangled, were trimmed and brushed.

Eleanor Strong was proud of her handsome hunter, and took many long rides during the sunny autumn days. Her father often accompanied her, riding a big Irish hunter. When Dick first saw this horse gallop across a field and leap a high fence, he showed that he had not forgotten Daisy's accident. As Mr. Strong and his mount galloped away, Dick followed eagerly and Eleanor, hoping that Dick would jump, gave him his head. But before he reached the fence, the chestnut hunter stopped suddenly and began to tremble. "Never mind, Dickie, you and I will try some jumps when no one can see us," said Eleanor, patting Dick's shoulder encouragingly.

Ever since the girl had heard Dick's story from Jack Davis, she had wished that she could have an opportunity to cure the hunter of his fear. Now that Dick was her own, Eleanor wanted to be able to enter him in horse shows, and she felt that he would do anything she wanted him to.

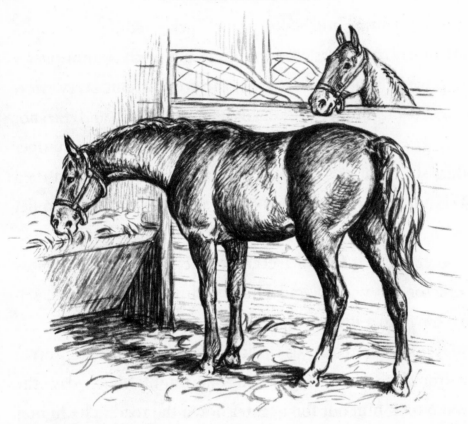

Dick's wish had always been to please his riders, and he was very fond of the girl who treated him so kindly. But when, one cloudy afternoon, she urged him to jump a low stone wall, the hunter again balked. Each day Eleanor tried patiently, patting and encouraging Dick, feeding him apples and sugar, and at last dismounting and leading him over a rail placed a short distance from the ground. But every effort to make the hunter take a high jump failed, and Eleanor sadly gave up trying. The girl often rode a young jumper when she went out with her father cross country, and then Dick was left in the stable or out in a pasture with a few quiet cows.

Soon after the first of December the Strongs went to New York for the winter, and Dick, with the other horses, settled down to a life of idleness.

Dick's winter coat was thick and furry, and he had grown fat from lack of exercise when, one bright March day, the groom took him out for a canter down the road. The hunter was hot and muddy when the man brought him back an hour later, and he felt uncomfortably warm in his stall, with a heavy blanket on.

"We can't send you to Miss Eleanor in New York unless

you are in good condition," said the groom as he rubbed down Dick's muddy legs. Each day he was given exercise and a good grooming. The heavy blanket helped to get rid of his thick hair, and by early April Dick's muscles were hard and his coat was shining again.

When Eleanor Strong came into the livery stable in New York, to which Dick had been sent the day before, the handsome hunter greeted her with a happy whinny. He had felt homesick in the strange stable, and he was delighted to see his mistress.

"Come on, Dick," said the girl, as she mounted him, "we will show the people in the park what a really good hunter looks like."

As Eleanor turned Dick into the street to ride the few blocks to Central Park, he was so startled and surprised by the traffic that he pranced along nervously, snorting and tossing his head. Eleanor held the reins firmly, talking quietly to steady Dick, and the hunter obeyed his mistress.

Once in the park the girl always let Dick have a good gallop, and he enjoyed these early spring mornings, when the cool air smelled of new grass and freshly budding trees. There were many other riders on the bridle paths, and Dick felt a thrill when sometimes several rode in a group, for it reminded him of the gathering of horses and riders at a hunt meet in Virginia.

One warm morning in May, Eleanor took Dick out for a last ride in the park. The next day the Strongs were to go back to the farm for the summer, and Dick would again have the freedom of wide pastures. The hunter was cantering gaily along a familiar path when he suddenly threw up his head and stopped so abruptly that Eleanor nearly fell off.

"*What* is the matter, Dick?" the girl said, annoyed and surprised at Dick's unusual action.

When the girl urged Dick forward, he refused to move, and continued to gaze at a group of people and horses which were some distance away on the bridle path. In the hunter's

eyes was a frightened expression and Eleanor was puzzled. Dismounting, she led the reluctant horse towards the distant group and, as she came nearer, she saw the reason for Dick's fear—a horse was on the ground, struggling to rise, and Eleanor realized that the chestnut hunter had again been re-minded of Daisy's accident. Dick and Eleanor reached the others just as the horse managed to stand up, and his rider, none the worse for the fall, led him away.

Dick was now beginning to grow more quiet, though he still started nervously at any sudden move. Eleanor was about to mount him and ride away, when the hunter, with a wild call, jerked the reins out of the girl's hand, and galloped after a horse which was trotting away from the scene of the accident. At Dick's call the horse stopped and answered, and the chestnut hunter, with a soft whinny of happiness, sniffed at her velvety nose and found that she *was* Daisy! With a sigh of contentment he laid his neck across her shoulders, and all his fear was forgotten in the joy of being with his sister again. Daisy's young rider was astonished at Dick's actions; but Eleanor, knowing the hunter's story, and seeing how much the two horses resembled each other, realized, with a thrill of excitement, that Dick had found his sister.

When the girl mounted Dick and tried to ride him away from Daisy, the horses refused to leave each other, so the boy on Daisy and Eleanor on Dick rode side by side to the entrance to the park.

With some difficulty Eleanor finally made Dick go back to his stable, where she stayed with him for some time, trying to quiet his excitement.

"Poor Dick," she said, as she patted his neck, "I'm sorry you ever saw Daisy again, for you were learning to be happy without her. Now you will have to forget her once more; tomorrow you are going back to the farm."

That night Dick refused all food, and when he was taken out of a trailer at the farm next day, he was hungry and tired.

The familiar stable and his big stall somewhat comforted Dick, and he ate part of the bran mash which he found in his manger. But he would not settle down quietly, and his anxious calls disturbed the other horses. At night the hunter pawed the floor restlessly, scattering his bed of deep straw about the stall.

Eleanor rode Dick every day, hoping that exercise would bring back his appetite, and these gallops with his mistress gave Dick his only happiness.

As the days went by, Dick grew thinner, and Eleanor was worried. All his life the chestnut hunter had been a happy, willing worker; even after he left Blithewood, he had given cheerful service to his owners. But his faithful heart had never forgotten Daisy, and now that he had seen her again, Dick's longing for her companionship was at last breaking his spirit.

CHAPTER XI

ONE afternoon, several weeks after Dick and Daisy met in the park, Eleanor and her father stood by the pasture gate, watching the hunter as he nibbled at the grass. Dick was thin, and his chestnut coat had lost much of its shining beauty.

Eleanor called, and Dick walked slowly to the gate. Putting his head over the girl's shoulder, the hunter sighed deeply, and Eleanor's eyes filled with tears as she stroked his neck.

"You are such a dear, beautiful horse, Dickie," she said. "It is too bad you are so unhappy. If *only* you could have Daisy with you again." Eleanor paused and looked expectantly at her father.

"If you are *both* going to cry, I suppose I will have to let

you have your way," said Mr. Strong. "But you must prom-
ise, Eleanor, not to fall in love with any more horses; the
stable is too full now."

"Very well, we will send for Daisy," he added; and Dick

jumped back in surprise at Eleanor's exclamation of delight.

Daisy's young rider had given Eleanor the name and address of the stable where Daisy was kept, and soon arrangements to buy the mare were under way.

On a bright June morning a week later, Dick heard Eleanor's voice at the stable door. A heavy rain had kept the horses under cover for two days, and the hunter welcomed the prospect of a canter with his mistress on his back.

Soon Dick was trotting down a lane which led to the big pasture at the back of the farm. The grass and leaves sparkled in the cool, rain-washed air, and wind-driven clouds made swiftly moving shadows on the blue hills. The hunter breathed deeply of the sweet air, and broke into a canter. Always sensitive to the mood of his rider, Dick felt that Eleanor was in high spirits, and he quickly responded. Through a grove of maple trees, where the moss-covered lane was soft under his hoofs, and on past a small pond went Dick, until he came in sight of the pasture gate.

Suddenly he stopped and threw up his head, listening intently. Then the call which Dick had heard came again, and he answered wildly.

Eleanor just had time to settle herself in the saddle before Dick jumped forward. Straight towards the gate he galloped; then with a splendid leap, he was over it and in the pasture, galloping towards Daisy!

There she stood, with her beautiful neck arched, and her brown eyes shining. As Dick came near, she gave a low whinny and trotted forward to meet her brother.

When Dick and Eleanor went back along the lane, Daisy was trotting beside them. Through the stable door she followed Dick, and she tried to squeeze herself into the same stall with him. Eleanor and the groom persuaded the mare to go in a stall next to Dick, and the two horses put their heads over the sides of the stall, and laid their noses against each other's necks. At last they were together again, and both were content.

Then Eleanor turned to her father, who was watching the horses, and told him the wonderful news of Dick's splendid jump. "I'm so glad that Daisy was put out in the pasture when she arrived last evening," she said. "If the horses had met in the stable, Dick would not have gone over the gate with me. Now my beautiful Dick is a jumper again!"

On a warm afternoon in August, nearly two months after Daisy had arrived at the Strongs' farm, Dick was trotting up the road towards home. The hunter was hot and rather weary, for he was returning from a near-by horse show, where there had been many difficult jumps to test his skill. Eleanor was on Dick's back, and as they neared the house and stables she leaned down to pat his wet shoulder.

"I'm *so* proud of you, Dickie," said the girl. "You won first prize in all the classes for hunters today; before long you will be a champion." Dick tossed his head, and answered happily when Daisy called from the stable.

Later that evening Dick and Daisy were led down the lane

and turned out in the big pasture. Both horses rolled on the ground, and then began cropping the grass which was wet with dew.

Dick and Daisy loved this upland pasture, and spent many happy years there together, for they were never parted again.

Often, when they were wanted for the saddle, the horses would be found standing under a maple tree on a hillside. Dick's neck would be across Daisy's shoulder, and in the eyes of both, as they dreamily gazed at the green fields and blue hills, would be the same happy expression that had been in the eyes of two colts when they lived in the wide meadows of Blithewood.